MW00904091

Little Tiger

Respect

STEVE DOHERTY AND
OLIVIA DYBIK

Published by Author Academy Elite, P.O. Box 43, Powell, OH 43035. www.authoracademyelite.com

Permission to use facsimiles of Taekwondo classes and Little Tiger educational material is authorized by Supreme Grandmaster Joon P. Choi, 10th Dan, Oriental Martial Arts College, 1349 Brice Road, Reynoldsburg, Ohio 43068. The Oriental Martial Arts College's Little Tiger and Taekwondo Program have been composed and developed by SGM Joon P. Choi from1963 to present time.

Printed in the United States of America

Paperback: 978-1-64085-565-6
Hardback: 978-1-64085-566-3
Ebook: 978-1-64085-567-0

Library of Congress Control Number: 2019931058

FORWARD

In today's society, many children struggle with criticism, hostility, ridicule, shame, and intolerance. As a result, these children suffer from low self-esteem and lack the confidence to succeed in life.

As parents and martial arts instructors, we work hard to correct these deficiencies. To help students learn to be respectful, we show respect to everyone. We teach discipline by demonstrating how we follow instructions and pay attention. We teach self-control by patiently listening, so we may understand the meaning and the desire of those who speak. To explain persistence, we show students that no athlete or martial artist begins with perfect form and flawless technique; instead, it is 'not quitting' that makes an athlete and martial artist great. By encouraging and praising students when they do something right, we teach confidence. And we offer approval, so students learn to like and love themselves as well as others.

Steve Doherty and Olivia Dybik have specifically written their Little Tiger Book Series to help young children understand and comprehend the life principles they teach in Taekwondo. They also designed the series to make reading more fun and enjoyable.

The principles taught in this series are not only important to students of Taekwondo but all children everywhere.

JOON P. CHOI, Supreme Grandmaster—
10th Dan Taekwondo

DEDICATION

Little Tiger—Respect is dedicated to Grace Savage—a
beautiful mother, grandmother, and great-grandmother.
Grace raised three children and fourteen foster children in
her lifetime, several of whom were special-needs children.
Grace had a loving, brave, and compassionate heart, and an
extraordinary talent for helping others. We miss you, Mo.

"Alright, class. Everyone gather around.
Have a seat on the floor, if you like,"
Mr. Steve says.

When he has everyone's attention,
Mr. Steve asks, "What do we teach
about how to treat people?"

Olivia, an eleven-year-old student, says, "We should always treat people with kindness and respect."

"What is respect?" Cade asks.

"Well, Cade, respect is how you feel about someone and how well you treat them," Olivia says.

"Is bowing to our instructors a form of respect?" Cade asks.

"Yes, silly," says his sister Addilyn. "We also bow to the American and Korean flags. That shows respect, too."

"And we say *Yes, sir and Yes, ma'am,* to our instructors. That shows respect, too," Gabby adds.

"That's right," Mr. Steve says. "We show respect by our actions as well as our words. When you respect others, you encourage them to respect you back."

"Respect sounds easy," Cade replies.

"It is easy. When we respect others,
it shows that we value who they are,"
Mr. Steve says.

"That's why respect is so important to being a Guardian of Peace," Olivia says.

"Can anyone become a Guardian of Peace?" Gabby asks.

"Yes, Gabby, if they learn and practice
the Guardian of Peace principles,"
Mr. Steve replies.

"What kind of principles?"
Addilyn asks.

"You just learned something about respect. The other principles are in the Korean *words of wisdom* that you have learned," replies Mr. Steve.

"You mean like discipline?"
Gabby asks.

"And self-control," says Cade.

"And confidence," adds Addilyn.

"You all learn very fast," Mr. Steve says. "Why don't we do our meditation and end class."

After two minutes of meditation,
Mr. Steve says, "Stand up. Let's
bow out."

At the end of every class, students
show respect by bowing to the
American and Korean flags.

And they show respect by facing their
instructor and bowing.

ABOUT THE AUTHORS

Steve Doherty is a retired United States Air Force officer and the author of four historical fiction thrillers. Steve obtained his undergraduate degree from Texas State University, earned a master's degree from Chapman University, and completed post-graduate studies in adult education at The Ohio State University. Steve lives in New Albany, Ohio, where he is a 1st Dan Instructor in Taekwondo.

Olivia Dybik is a seventh-grade student at New Albany Middle School, in New Albany, Ohio, where she is a 'Straight A' student. She a 1st Gup (Stripped Black Belt) in Taekwondo. She is a summer reading volunteer at the New Albany Library and a volunteer at the annual Arnold SportsWorld Kids & Teens Expo. Olivia has a passion for art and helping others.

RESPECT DISCUSSION QUESTIONS

1. You can start with a simple definition that children can understand. Respect means: 1) how you feel about someone, and, 2) how you treat them.

2. Questions to ask your child:

   a. What are some good examples of respect?

      i. Listening to someone speak without interrupting.

      ii. Walk on the sidewalk rather than on someone's yard.

      iii. Saying "Thank you" when someone does something nice for you.

   b. Why is it important to show respect?

      i. Respecting others is a way of expressing our feelings for them.

      ii. Respect can build a strong relationship between people.

      iii. When a person shows respect for someone, it means that the person respected has value to you.

c. What does it mean to show respect?

    i. Respect is a way of treating or thinking about something or someone.

    ii. People respect others who are impressive for any number of reasons, such as being in authority — like a teacher or a policeman — or being older — like a grandparent.

    iii. You show respect by being polite and kind.

d. What are the benefits of respect?

    i. Respect improves your image.

    ii. It increases student and teacher engagement.

    iii. It creates a fair environment.

e. How can we show respect?

    i. Be polite. Say "Yes, sir," and "No, sir."

    ii. Be helpful. Pick up your clothes and toys.

    iii. Say, "Thank you." Let someone know that they are appreciated.

LITTLE TIGER SERIES™ BOOKS COMING SOON

Little Tiger — Guardian of Peace

Little Tiger — Discipline

Little Tiger — Confidence

Little Tiger — Self-Control

Little Tiger — Persistence

Little Tiger — Courage

Little Tiger — Compassion

Little Tiger — Integrity

Little Tiger — Indomitable Spirit

AUTHOR'S NOTES

We appreciate your purchase of our book, *Little Tiger—Respect*. When you finish reading it, we would be grateful if you would take time and post a review on Amazon.com. It is the best way to provide us with your feedback.

ACKNOWLEDGMENT

Olivia and I would like to give a special thanks to our Taekwondo leader, Supreme Grandmaster Joon Pyo Choi (10th Dan), Founder and President of Oriental Martial Arts College (OMAC) in Reynoldsburg, Ohio. The Taekwondo and Little Tiger programs that SGM Choi developed, his vision, teachings, philosophy, and guidance, are at the heart of these books. We are grateful that he has allowed us to bring the life principles that he promotes to millions of children around the world through the medium of children's books. We are thrilled that our children's books can contribute to and be a small part of his historic legacy, and we are proud to be part of his worldwide organization.

SGM Joon Pyo Choi
ww.omacworld.com
OMAC

Since founding OMAC in 1963, SGM Choi has taught over 25,000 students, including twenty U.S. National champions and Olympic medalists. He won the Korean National Championships in 1967 and 1968. In 1979, SGM Choi was the head coach of the U.S. National Taekwondo Team and received Coach of the Year honors. He coached the American Olympic Taekwondo Team at the 1988 Seoul Korea Olympic Games where the U.S. women's team took the Gold Medal, and the U.S. men's team won the Silver Medal. The U.S. Team won a total of four Gold, two Silver, and five Bronze medals.

SGM Choi's achievements span the global community, and he is active in national and international committees covering martial arts, business, and nonprofit organizations. In 1976, SGM Choi formed the Battle of Columbus (BOC) Martial Arts Championship. In 2001, he merged the BOC with the Arnold Sports Festival USA and serves as the chairman of the Arnold Battle of Columbus Martial Arts World Games held annually in Columbus, Ohio.